THE SCHOLARSHIP WORKBOOK

JESSICA JOHNSON

A 3-step scholarship tutorial, created by the recipient of more than $200,000 in scholarships

LEARN HOW TO

Identify Tailor-Made Scholarship Opportunities
Determine Your Scholarship Profile
Write Winning Essays
Maximize Your Scholarship Eligibility

THE
SCHOLARSHIP
ACADEMY

The Scholarship Academy acknowledges the financial support of the Gannett Foundation. Special thanks to the Herb Block Foundation.

Cover design and editing by the WhiteHorse Company
Printed by the WhiteHorse Company
www.whitehorsecompany.com

CONTENTS

Section Three: Closing the Deal

Jessica's Extras

INTRODUCTION

Greetings! I am so excited that you have decided to take this 12-step journey with me! As a recipient of more than $200,000 in scholarships, I know how anxious you are to get this process underway. For the last nine years, I have been working with schools, churches, and youth groups to prepare students for scholarship success. Through a series of workshops, individual consultations, and trainings, my nonprofit organization, The Scholarship Academy, has worked tirelessly to prove to "average" students that finding money for college is a realistic possibility.

The Scholarship Workbook is a compilation of my personal experiences, research, and client success stories. Over the years, students who participated in our Scholarship Boot Camp have helped us hone in on the activities that accomplish our core vision of *transforming average students into exemplary models of leadership, scholarship and sevanthood.*

After serving on several scholarship committees, I realized that most students lacked basic concepts that lead to creating winning scholarship packages. Students with great scholarship profiles did not know how to "sell themselves" to scholarship committees. Students with lackluster profiles simply had nothing to write about that was substantial. *The Scholarship Workbook* will help you put the pieces together.

Each section of *The Scholarship Workbook* is broken down into weekly and biweekly activities designed to help you identify unique opportunities to maximize your funding potential.

- **Section One** focuses on helping students identify their passions. The activities presented in this section lay the foundation for creating a solid scholarship profile.

- **Section Two** outlines the scholarship search process, breaking it down into realistic terms. Each lesson will teach you how to identify the scholarships that you have a stronger chance of winning.

- **Section Three** shows you how to create a winning scholarship essay. From start to finish, this section will walk you through the development of essays that are sure to get you noticed.

Along the way, you will get to read a few examples of projects that win, and receive guidance on ways to shape your own winning project. You can also refer to the appendix of *The Scholarship Workbook* for additional tips and my list of favorite scholarships.

The perfect time to follow this 3-step program would be at the beginning of your junior year, but if you have already passed that mark, DON'T PANIC! The best thing about *The Scholarship Workbook* is that you can work at your own pace.

If you have already completed the steps in the first section, fast-forward through that section until you get to where you need to be. A large portion of this workbook involves setting goals and developing a concrete college funding strategy.

Alright, let's get started! Before you begin, I would like to share my scholarship success story with you to give you a little motivation.

JESSICA'S STORY

I am a native of Jackson, Tennessee. As the daughter of two educators, I always knew I was going to college, but paying for it was another story. I decided that I did not want my parents to have to make sacrifices to send me to school. I began to think of ways that I could use my talents to increase my funding opportunities.

Since the age of twelve, I have had a sincere passion for the arts, especially theater arts and public speaking. I decided to explore opportunities to make myself stand out in these areas. My golden opportunity came at one of the most unsuspecting moments. During my eighth grade year, I learned that a close friend was considering joining a gang. In a city as small as Jackson, I thought this was a ridiculous idea. So, I thought of ways to talk him out of it. When it seemed that talking was ineffective, I turned to writing. Before I knew it, I had created an entire play exposing the effects of gang involvement. My best friend gave the script to the school's theater director, and the rest is history. My play was produced at my middle school, won a local playwriting competition, and showcased at the local theater. People started to ask, "Who is Jessica Johnson?"

I gathered my friends and formed the group Alternative to Violence. We performed a series of improvisational skits based on issues affecting teenagers. After each performance, we challenged audience members to commit to gang- and drug-free lives.

My reputation as a youth leader was established. I sought new issues to tackle. When I entered the ninth grade, I narrowed my career choices to the field of communications. I thought of ways I could combine my love for the community with my newfound interest in communications.

One Sunday morning, I was listening to the local radio station's talk show and, once again, they were discussing the state of youth in our community. It frustrated me how the focus was on youth who were doing negative things. What about the youth who were doing positive things? I scheduled a meeting with the station owner, and the next week I was on air with my first radio talk show, *Teen Talk*. The radio show was on air for one year on Saturday mornings, and it covered everything from dating and stereotypes to selecting the right college.

After the radio talk show, I decided to start *Teens Speak*, a column in our local newspaper, to highlight other teens doing positive things in our community. By the time I was ready to graduate high school, I was producing short documentaries for the nationally syndicated television network Oxygen Media.

The first scholarship I received was $20,000 from React Magazine for my community involvement. I was only a junior, and this first success was enough to push me into full force. My second major scholarship was the Discover Card Tribute Award to the tune of $17,500. After receiving several local scholarships, including the JC Penney Golden Rule Award, I was accepted into Howard University on a full-tuition-and-room academic scholarship, and I was financially set for 4 years of college.

The following page is dedicated to estimating how much you will need in financial aid to cover your college costs. Sit down with your parents and estimate your complete financial aid package.

The scholarship process truly starts with you becoming a knowledgeable consumer. If you do not know how much your college tuition actually costs, how can you possibly set realistic college funding goals? Use the How Am I Going To Pay? worksheet on the following page to map out the costs and potential funding opportunities that will jump-start your scholarship process.

How Am I Going to Pay?

This exercise will help you estimate how much financial aid you will need to cover your college costs. Sit down with your parents and estimate your complete financial aid package.

The scholarship process truly starts with you becoming a knowledgeable consumer. If you do not know how much your college tuition actually costs, how can you possibly set realistic college funding goals? Use this worksheet to map the costs and potential funding opportunities that will jump-start your scholarship process.

My Dream School _____

The Cost $ _____

My Scholarship Goal $ _____

Potential Financial Aid

    Pell Grant (up to $5,500) $ _____

    Federal Supplemental Educational Grant (up to $4,000) $ _____

    Academic Competitiveness Grant ($750) $ _____

    SMART Grant (up to $4,000) $ _____

    Federal Work-Study Program (stipend) $ _____

Total Federal Aid $ _____

Potential State-Based Aid (refer to website given by your state)

    Philadelphia Academic Excellence Scholarship ($1,500) $ _____

    Philadelphia State Grant (Up to $4,500) $ _____

    Beneficial Scholars Program ($5000) $ _____

Local Aid

    _____ $ _____

    _____ $ _____

Grand Total

    _____ $ _____

    _____ $ _____

SECTION ONE

Identifying Your Passion

LESSON ONE

Identifying Your Passion

Everyone has passions. Perhaps your passion is writing, acting, dancing or playing a sport. Think about your hobbies and the correlation of those hobbies to your career aspirations. These elements are the gateway to your scholarship success. The most successful scholarship applicants have simply figured out ways to use their skills, talents, and passions in a manner that have an impact on the lives of those around them.

Scholarship committees are searching for students who are worthy investments. In exchange for their donation, they are seeking students who will give them future bragging rights. The activities that you participate in today will give the scholarship committee a sneak peek at your potential.

Take a moment and write down those things that you enjoy doing. Then select one activity you are passionate about and begin brainstorming ways to turn that passion into a platform for winning scholarships.

Create a List of Your Talents

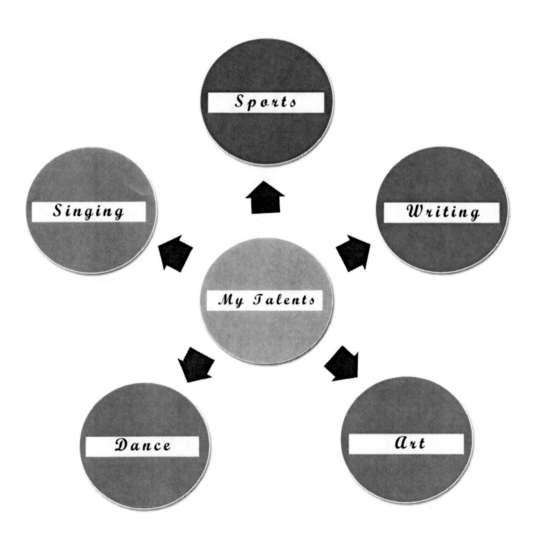

Activity 1:
Create a List of Your Talents

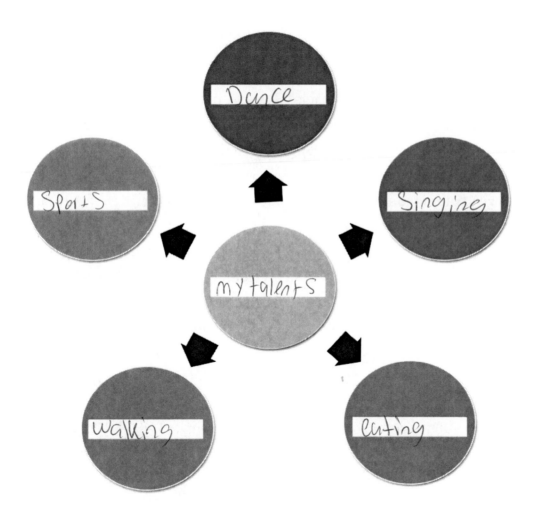

LESSON TWO

Determining Your Scholarship Profile

Many students get frustrated and overwhelmed by the entire scholarship application process, because they fail to consider what they bring to the table. Instead of randomly applying for every scholarship available, it is important to focus on the scholarships that are already looking for your particular profile. Why?

Determining your scholarship profile will help you create a comprehensive package to submit to scholarship committees. Instead of trying to figure out who you are and what is great about you, scholarship committees can easily spot a student who has maintained a constant streamline of activities and experiences that support their stated goals. When a committee is able to quickly connect the dots and get a full picture of a student's it factor, it makes it easier to justify their investment. For example, if a student is interested in journalism, but all of the summer programs and club activities involved math and science, there is a disconnect that could lead to more questions from a committee instead of higher scores.

Establishing a scholarship profile will also help you narrow down your scholarship application pool. Instead of submitting 150 *maybe* scholarships, you can use your scholarship profile to look for the scholarship programs that are tailored just for you.

What is your scholarship profile? Are you an athlete who took time to start up a little league team in your neighborhood? Are you an artist who established your own business? Below you will find a list of the Top 12 Scholarship Profiles. Think about the profile that resembles your winning qualities, and then brainstorm ways to take your profile to the next level.

Top 12 Scholarship Profiles

1. **The Academic Achiever:** This individual shines both in the class and in the community. His intellect inspires others to strive for success.

2. **The Outstanding Leader:** This individual has learned how to lead others in a manner that focuses on the power of combined strengths.

3. **The Service Guru:** The Service Guru is known for launching projects that transform the lives of those around them.

4. **The Compassionate Giver:** This individual takes the art of giving to a new level. Her unselfish spirit is virtually contagious.

5. **The Overcomer:** This individual is genuinely admired for his ability to transform obstacles into opportunities. They sky is the limit because he knows that failure is not an option.

6. **The Creator:** Originality and passion are two qualities that will always set her apart from the crowd. She is not afraid to get rid of the drum and following the beats of her heart.

7. **The Career Guide:** Internships, summer programs, pre-college organizations, you name it, she's a part of it. Her strong desire to pursue a career creates a solid path to occupational success.

8. **The Community Organizer:** Injustices do not stand a chance against this young revolutionary. His youthful energy and commitment to the common good can be found at the forefront of a community's most pressing issues.

9. **The Muse:** The arts are his playground, and there is truly none like him. He sets the tone for youthful expression.

10. **The Adventurer:** This individual has taken life's journey abroad. Whether it is taking much-needed medical supplies to South Africa or teaching English to students in Spain, this person is not afraid to create their own boundaries.

11. **The Scientific Master:** The Scientific Master knows how to mix up the right ingredients to claim success! Summer programs, internships and hands-on scientific experience easily puts her at the front of the class.

12. **The Math Magician:** Manipulating numbers is not just a game for this individual; it is a way of life. He knows how to make his love for numbers truly count!

My Scholarship Profile

ACADEMIC

Beyond your GPA, what makes you stand out from other applicants? Did you overcome an obstacle to maintain your GPA?

1. _____
2. _____
3. _____

COMMUNITY SERVICE

How many people did your project reach? What tangible results were produced?

1. _____
2. _____
3. _____

LEADERSHIP

How have you impacted others? What changes occurred as a result of your leadership?

1. _____
2. _____
3. _____

SPECIAL INTEREST

Have you used your talent to help others? Have you received any special awards?

1. _____

2. _____

3. _____

OBSTACLES TO OVERCOME

Have you overcome severe obstacles and still managed to succeed? What have you learned from your experiences?

1. _____

2. _____

3. _____

Determining The Scholarship Profile

Activity 2:
Select your scholarship profile and write a 300-word statement about your "winning qualities"

_____

_____

_____

_____

_____

_____

_____

_____

_____

_____

_____

_____

_____

_____

_____

_____

_____

_____

_____

_____

_____

_____

_____

_____

_____

_____

_____

_____

_____

_____

_____

_____

_____

LESSON THREE

Get Involved!

Chances are you may have had a slightly difficult time articulating the qualities that would make you stand out from other applicants. One of the best ways for a scholarship committee to gain a solid understanding of your overall character is simply to examine what you do in your free time. While it might be tempting to join ten organizations, participate in a host of summer camps from the arts to pre-engineering, and log in hundreds of community service hours, the reality is that top scholarship applicants often have a common, simple theme.

The savvy scholarship applicant will attempt to focus on the activities that highlight one of four major areas: their leadership capabilities, a special talent, a special interest such as the environment or health, or their solid civic commitment.

Start with your school and find out which organizations are related to your passion. If you enjoy public speaking, does your school have a debate team? If not, whom could you talk to about getting one started? Maybe you are more interested in the arts or the sciences. Are these clubs at your school? What about your community?

Your goal for this week is simply identify existing organizations that will help you further develop your talents. Instead of randomly signing up for an activity, use the following extra-curricular activities matrix to keep your engagement focused, balanced and purposeful.

Extra-Curricular Activities

There are a number of school and community-based organizations with national affiliations that offer scholarships. Your early involvement in these organizations is sure to put you on track for access to specialized scholarship options.

If you are interested in a particular organization, and it does not exist in your school or your community, find out what it would take to start a local chapter. What better way to show initiative and leadership than to *start* an organization in your school or community? Remember, the number one characteristic that attracts scholarship committees is an individual's ability to take initiative!

School and Community-Based Organizations with National Affiliations

SCHOOL-BASED	COMMUNITY-BASED
Future Business Leaders of America	Boys and Girls Club of America
Mu Alpha Theta	Jack and Jill
Debate Team	Beta Club
HOSA	NAACP
DECA	National Urban League
National Honors Society	Girls Scouts/Boy Scouts of America

Activity 3:
Create your extra-curricular Activities matrix

Activities that demonstrate leadership:
1)
2)
3)
4)

Activities that highlight your special talent:
1)
2)
3)
4)

Activities that exemplify your special interest:
1)
2)
3)
4)

Activities that showcase your civic commitment:
1)
2)
3)
4)

LESSON FOUR

Backing It All Up

Now that you have taken the first steps in developing your personal profile, it is time to focus on more aggressive scholarship preparation tactics. It's no longer enough just to be a member of an organization or have a high G.P.A. Scholarship committees are looking for students with strong leadership and community backgrounds. They want people who have identified a need in their community and addressed that need in a unique way. In short, visiting the nursing home at Christmas will never win you a $20,000 scholarship! You must dig deep and come up with something creative.

So where do you start? Read the following samples of winning projects. Then take a few days to come up with your own *Brag Project*. This project will serve as the main topic of your scholarship essays.

Create Your Own Program/Business

 Local Psychology Club—Organize a group of your classmates who are interested in the psychology field and host monthly sessions with psychologists as guest speakers.

 Youth Arts and Crafts Business—Start making money for your favorite pastime. You could easily sell your unique creations to church members and, of course, your friends. To put a community service spin on it, you can donate a portion of your proceeds to a local worthy cause or teach younger children how to do your craft.

 Leaders of Tomorrow Program—Organize a group of your friends and plan a few events that will prove to your community that you all are the Leaders of Tomorrow.

 Computer Programming for the Elderly—Technology rules. If you are a computer genius (or you at least know the basics), introduce a group of senior citizens to the wonderful Internet highway. They will never stop thanking you.

Mentor Younger Children

 "Books and Balls' Program—Sometimes the best way to get through to youth is through the activities that they love. You could easily organize an after-school program at a community service center that would encourage young people to read and study by making it a requirement before they can play ball.

 Back to the Future Program—Grab a few of your friends and connect them with students from your local elementary school. Organize monthly events that will leave a lasting impact on our future.

Use Talents (Art, Dance, etc.) to Benefit the Community

 Start a Team Theatre Group—If drama is more your speed, organize a few of your friends and create skits that expose the effects of drug and alcohol use.

 Organize a Fashion Show—If you are known for having flare or you have a knack for design, talk to your advisor about organizing a fashion show at your school. The proceeds can be donated to the nonprofit organization of your choice.

 Use Artwork to Speak Your Mind—Encourage your art class to create a mural that represents the voices of the students at your school. You can work with your art teacher to organize an official presentation of the mural to one of your local council

What Have Others Done?

For the last few years, the news has been plastered with stories of students who have managed to accumulate up to a million dollars in scholarship offers. How did they do it?

When you are thinking about using your passions to help your community, you do not have to reinvent the wheel. Take time to research projects that others have done that enabled them to win scholarships. The following scholarship programs have profiles of previous scholarship winners:

- AXA Achievement Awards (www.axa-achievement.org)

- Ron Brown Scholars (www.ronbrown.com)

- Discover Card Tribute Award (www.discoverfinancial.com)

- Gates Millennium Scholars Program (www.gmsp.org)

- Prudential Spirit of Community Awards (www.prudential.com/spirit)

Once you've had an opportunity to read through a few winning project ideas, use the form provided to begin brainstorming your own Scholarship Brag Project.

Useful Websites

www.youthnoise.com

www.PointsofLight.org

www.thevolunteercenter.org

Did You Know?

You can receive grant money to implement your unique community service idea. Use these smaller awards to help you build your scholarship resume and create a solid foundation for the top scholarship dollars.

Here are a few websites that will provide you with information on funding opportunities:

www.dosomething.org

www.idealist.org

www.ysa.org

Activity 4:
Create your own
Scholarship brag project

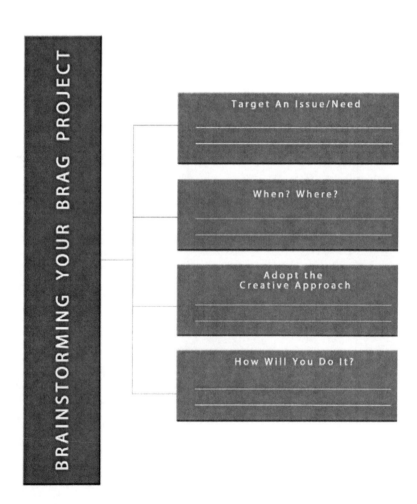

BRAINSTORMING YOUR BRAG PROJECT

Target An Issue/Need

When? Where?

Adopt the
Creative Approach

How Will You Do It?

Project Steps

1. **Target an issue or need in your community.** Identify something that you would like to change (pollution, homelessness).

2. **Brainstorm the Creative Approach.** Find a different way to bring a new touch to serving your community that helps express who you are (i.e., if you are an artist, consider having a community exhibit with proceeds benefiting your cause).

3. **Plan the Details.** Think about how you are going to organize this project and the people and/or organizations in your community that you already have relationships with to help you cut costs (i.e., churches, family members' organizations or jobs, etc.).

When?

Make a timeline that sets realistic dates for your goals to be completed (i.e., August: Talk to my coach about starting a recycling center. September 1: Have at least two school athletic teams signed up to participate. September 15: Recycling Center Kick Off).

Where?

Think about good locations for your event that fit the need for your project, areas that will allow you to set up for free or at little cost. Also determine if they will be willing to allow you set up on more than one occasion, if necessary (YMCA, churches, community centers).

Connecting the Dots Worksheet
My Interests/Talents Are...

I could help the people in my community by

1. _____
2. _____
3. _____
4. _____

Project Details

1. Whom would you help? _____
2. How long would the project last? What specific days? _____
3. What location could you use for your project? _____
4. Whom could you get to help you with the project? _____

Project Timeline

By _____ (enter date) I will _____

By _____ (enter date) I will _____

By _____ (enter date) I will _____

By _____ (enter date) I will _____

Section One Wrap-Up

Your scholarship profile wouldn't be complete without the perfect mix of summer opportunities and career explorations. How serious are you about pursuing a particular field? Summer programs, job shadowing opportunities and internships are a perfect way to get a snapshot of your future. They are also a good way to showcase your commitment to your career goals to college and scholarship selection committees.

Try to find a summer program at one of the colleges that you are interested in attending. Colleges often use summer programs as preliminary recruiting opportunities. Making connections with colleges early is a sure method to at least get your foot in the door. To find out about summer programs, visit the web sites of the schools you are interested in attending. It might also be a good idea to look at your activities matrix and use the summer to fill in any major gaps.

Summer Program Resources

Organization	Web Site
Howard University's Summer Enrichment Programs	www.howard.edu
NBA Crump Law Camp	www.nationalbar.org/ crumplawcamp.html
Peterson's Summer Camps and Internships Guide	www.petersons.com
Top 100 Summer Programs for Minority High School Students	www.blackexcel.org
The Rockefeller University Science Outreach Program	www.rockefeller.edu/outreach
Boston University Research Internship Program for High School Students	www.bu.edu/summer/high-school-programs/ research-internshipl
Carnegie Mellon Summer Program	http://www.cmu.edu/ enrollment/pre-college
Johns Hopkins Center for Talented Youth	http://cty.jhu.edu
MITES: Minority Introduction to Engineering Entrepreneurship and Science	http://web.mit.edu/mites
CyberCamps	www.giantcampus.com/cybercamps/ index.asp
Georgetown International Relations Program for High School Students	http://scs.georgetown.edu/ courses/537/international-relations
Young Scholars and Writers Camp at Rhodes College	http://www.rhodes.edu/ English/4422.asp
Northwestern's Summer Theater Arts Program for High School Students	http://www.northwestern.edu/nhsi/

SECTION TWO

The Scholarship Search Begins

OVERVIEW

The Scholarship Search Process

Alright. So, you have gotten yourself together. Now what? This entire section is all about finding the scholarships that you are truly eligible to receive. Each lesson will explore a specific scholarship category.

Because there are hundreds of resources, websites and search engines, most students find the scholarship process overwhelming. Without a thoughtful strategy, an individual could easily apply for more than a hundred awards and not be successful. At The Scholarship Academy, our approach to scholarship research is simple: Take it one step at a time.

We have developed a 16-point Good Fit Theory that can be used to narrow your scholarship options. This section will teach you how to use these core areas to identify the awards that you truly have a stronger chance of winning.

LESSON ONE

Intro To The Scholarship Search Process

Books. Search Engines. Newsletters. Where do you begin? The diagram on the following page outlines the major areas for scholarship resources. Take a moment to put them in the order you believe they should be. What should be your first source of scholarship information?

_____

_____

_____

_____

_____

_____

_____

_____

_____

_____

_____

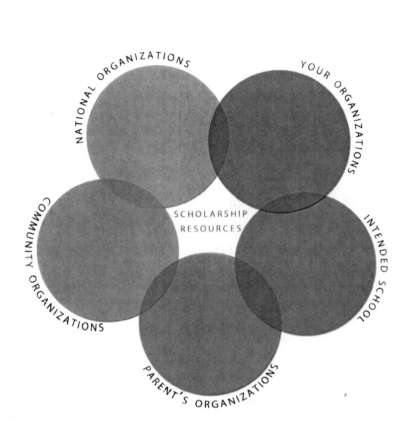

If you guessed that *your* school should be your first source, you are absolutely right! The first place that you should look for scholarships is your high school. Talk to your guidance counselor about the organizations at your school that provide scholarships. Students are often unaware that organizations such as the Key Club, Beta Club, Future Business Leaders of America, DECA, and the National Honors Society can provide them with funding for college. These scholarships are easier to receive because there are typically fewer applicants.

Additionally, there are a host of scholarships which use student nominations from guidance counselors and principals as part of the selection criteria . Find out about the nomination requirements for programs such as The Comcast Leaders and Achievers Program, the Kiwanis Leadership Scholarship, and the Posse Scholars Award. Your school may also have a special alumni scholarship fund in place. The goal is for you to acquire the easy dollars first.

Getting Started...

1. Your intended school or college is, of course, one of the most logical sources of scholarship information. Make sure you inquire about scholarships for incoming freshmen when you tour the campus, and work closely with your high school coach, band director, debate team leader, etc. to ensure that you are on track for tryouts and scholarship deadlines.

   One of the frequently untapped resources on the college campus is the Alumni Association. On many campuses, especially HBCU campuses, the Alumni Associations establish scholarship funds for both incoming freshmen and continuing students. Check with the Department of Alumni Relations at your top school choices.

2. Organizations in which you are already involved fall right into our Good Fit Theory, because you have probably spent a considerable amount of time building up your leadership and service profile through these programs. Outside of your school organizations, programs such as the NAACP, the Boys and Girls Club, and the YMCA provide scholarships exclusively for members.

 Identify scholarship opportunities within your prospective school and organizations.

LESSON TWO

*Using Your Scholarship Profile To Identify
Tailored Scholarship Options*

In the first section we introduced you to the 12 basic scholarship profiles. Your scholarship profile can be used to guide your scholarship search process. Let's use the Community Service Guru as an example. There are a large number scholarships that are "looking for students" who have implemented outstanding service ventures with lasting impact. In fact, some of these scholarships possibly may not strongly consider the GPA of a student who has mastered the art of giving. Read the sample scholarship profile below, and visit www.dosomething.org to identify scholarships that you think Samantha might be eligible to receive.

Samantha's Profile

Samantha is no stranger to obstacles. Growing up in a family of 7, she often witnessed her mother delicately balance their daily needs with their basic wants. An average student, Samantha knew that she couldn't rely on her 3.0 GPA alone to help her claim top scholarship dollars. In her social studies class, they were learning about the HIV/AIDS epidemic in Africa, and she wondered how the disease was impacting families who were impoverished. As she thought about all of the resources available in the U.S., she decided that one simple way she could help would be to collect toiletries from area hotels and hospitals, and have them sent to women and orphans impacted by the disease. She wrote a letter to the hotels and hospitals and she got her friends involved. Samantha was able to collect more than 1,000 items to send to an orphanage in Africa.

Scholarships Samantha Might Consider

_____

_____

_____

_____

Here Are A Few We Might Consider For Samantha:

- AXA Achievement Award
- Prudential Spirit of Community
- Best Buy
- Kohls' Kids Who Care Award

Research the scholarships that fit your scholarship profile.

LESSON THREE

Our Good Fit Theory

This diagram highlights the target scholarship research areas that will help you identify a tailored list of scholarship opportunities. Instead of using massive scholarship search engines, take time to research possible scholarship opportunities in each of these categories. You might be surprised to learn that there are a host of organizations in your community that offer major-specific scholarships, and there are national programs such as the KFC Scholars program that support your entrepreneurial spirit.

ARE YOU ELIGIBLE?

There is nothing more frustrating than spending countless hours working on an application that is not a good fit for you. Scholarship committees often set up their scoring sheets according to the eligibility criteria. If you do not meet the baseline requirements, especially for most national scholarship awards, you might want to focus your energies on the scholarships that are "looking for you."

Activity 5:
How do you rate?

For each scholarship that you are considering, go through each of the eligibility requirements and create your own checklist.

How do you rate?

Criteria	Max Score	Your Score
G.P.A.	10	
Test Score	10	
Leadership Role	20	
Community Service	25	
Financial Need	25	
Obstacles* *Special Circumstances/ Disabilities	10	
Total	100	

Other Key Scholarship Connections

Your parents' organizations and their places of employment can also serve as potential funding sources. Sororities, fraternities, and other community-based organizations provide scholarships for members' dependents. If you are planning to attend the same college that your parents attended, you might want to check to see if there are any special scholarship resources there. This week, have your parents ask around to see what they may be able to contribute to your search.

Community-based organizations represent a large pool of the scholarship dollars. Local department stores, civic organizations, churches, and banks all provide funding to prospective college students. You will notice that some of the resources are the same as the parent resources.

Tips For Finding Local Awards

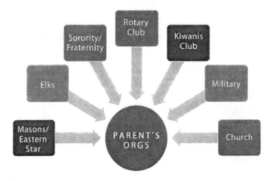

Sit down with your parents and make a list of the organizations they are affiliated with. Be sure to ask about special health conditions and extenuating family circumstances (i.e. adoptions, foster care, etc). Use this info to fill in your chart here.

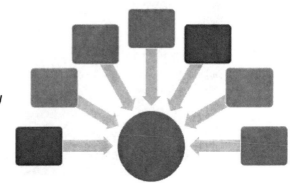

Tips For Finding Local Awards

✓ Contact your local chamber of commerce

✓ Visit the web sites of all the high schools in your community

✓ Find out if your city has a "community foundation"

✓ Look for local chapters of national organizations (e.g., the Memphis Chapter of the National Black MBA Association)

✓ Reach out to local credit unions

Add at least 5 local awards to your scholarship portfolio.

Finally, look at the major corporations that offer national scholarships. Naturally, these scholarships are much more competitive. Each year, thousands and thousands of students attempt to jump-start their scholarship application process with the more notable awards, such as the coveted Gates Millennium Scholarship and the Coca-Cola Scholars Award. When they do not win, they get discouraged and take out loans.

One of the reasons we emphasize starting with some of the smaller awards is that this approach will allow you to create a more competitive foundation for the top scholarship dollars. For instance, I received the $1,000 JC Penney Golden Rule Award. Although it was small, I used it as leverage to make myself look more attractive to major awards like Discover Card.

A large part of the scholarship process is being realistic about your funding potential. Take the Ron Brown Scholarship, for instance. This scholarship is targeted at students who demonstrate strong academic achievement, outstanding leadership, and community involvement. If your GPA is a 2.75 and your community involvement is low, but your leadership is high, should you still apply?

LESSON FOUR

Putting a Process to the Process

By now you should have a strong list of potential scholarship opportunities. With so many attachments, recommendation letters and transcript requests, the scholarship process can truly seem like a maze—but not if you get organized!

1. It is important that you begin to organize your list according to scholarship deadlines so that you will remain on track. Set personal and academic goals for yourself each month and begin matching up applications that require similar information. If a scholarship is due on, February 15, for instance, your personal deadline should be February 1 to have all documents completed so that someone can look over them before you submit them. Make sure you check out my Favorite Scholarships list at the end of this workbook to add to your scholarship calendar.

2. Many scholarships have a specific set of directions that you must follow. Some will deduct points for your failure to pay attention to details. Make a separate checklist of all the required materials, and have someone else sign off on them to make sure your entire application is complete.

3. Request at least five to seven copies of your official transcript ahead of time, so you will not have to wait on this item for your application

to be complete. You can also secure electronic versions of your recommendation letters (if your teachers feel comfortable with it), print them and have them ready to be signed and sealed for each new application.

4. Try to set aside one day each month on which to mail out batches of applications. This will keep you ahead of the game, and cut down on the possibility of you forgetting to include certain materials at the last minute.

 Create a Scholarship Calendar.

Sample Scholarship Calendar

OCTOBER						
Sunday	**Monday**	**Tuesday**	**Wednesday**	**Thursday**	**Friday**	**Saturday**
		1	**2** Start Prudential application online	**3**	**4**	**5**
6	**7** Secure 5 official transcripts	**8** Ask 2 teachers for recommendation letters	**9**	**10** Start Coca-Cola online application	**11**	**12**
13	**14** Make final edits to Prudential application	**15**	**16** Submit Coca-Cola application	**17**	**18** Draft VFW speech for competition	**19**
20	**21** Start Horatio Alger application	**22**	**23** Update scholarship profile	**24**	**25**	**26**
27	**28**	**29** Submit final Horatio application	**30**	**31**		

> **My goals for this month**
> - Identify 3 new scholarship opportunities
> - Run for a leadership position in FBLA
> - Start a draft of my career goals essay

Section Two Wrap-Up

The trick to finding scholarships is thinking outside of the box. Look for national organizations and corporations that are related to your field. Many organizations provide scholarships for students who want to study those particular fields. For instance, your state's National Education Association (NEA) chapter may offer scholarships for prospective teachers. The National Society of Black Engineers (NSBE) may offer awards for prospective engineers. Your mentor should be able to help you identify such organizations in your community.

It is very important that you make contact with your guidance counselor, because there are certain awards that only the counselor can nominate you to receive. One particular award that meets this criterion is the Comcast Leaders and Achievers Award. If you do not know your guidance counselor well, bring a copy of your resumé to share with your counselor and make it a point to get to know him or her this month, so they can write strong recommendation letters for you. The bottom line is that you should...**LEAVE NO STONE UNTURNED!**

Make an appointment with your guidance counselor.

Popular Scholarship Search Engines

Organization	Web Site
Black College Dollars	www.blackcollegedollars.org
Latino College Dollars	www.latinocollegedollars.org
Adventures in Education Scholarship Search	www.adventuresineducation.org
American Education Services Mentor	www.aessuccess.org
Scholarship Help and Advice Center	www.scholarshiphelp.org
United Negro College Fund	www.uncf.org
College Board Scholarship Search	www.collegeboard.com
College View an A-Z Scholarship List	www.collegeview.com
Federal Government Aid	www.federalstudentaid.ed.gov
Peterson's Scholarship Fund	www.petersons.com/finaid/
PrincetonReview.com Scholarship Search	www.princetonreview.com/finance
Scholarship Search	www.scholarships.com
FinAid	www.finaid.org
Scholarship Gateway	www.college-scholarships.com
Do Something	www.dosomething.org

SCHOLARSHIP SEEK-AND-FIND

```
B U R G E R K I N G O U H T G E R G V B H J K
A T G F D S G J U I T I O P P P O O P P O P U
N A G A T E S I I M I F I N N K P P G S I F R
K U I I W A L M A R T U E R T I Y H F H K I E
O V B F X Z S A D I G L K R G F R E U O P J A
F R Y U X Z V B H I E O I B N M Y R D D G H N
A D F G H J Y F G T Y H B J G D S A E D C L A
M I O P K K J H J K K L I L K G D S G J K L E
E L O Y G F R H C D I A Y G H Y E W S H I I A
R O N B R O W N Y R D F I C R T Y U I S E T G
I H B N G F R H N H J I J G K Y G T R E F G U
O M C A S T O Y O T A F C X C F T R T Y Y E
A L P T Y L E N O L U A T F G D I R S S L A
```

List of Scholarship Companies/Organizations

Bank of America
Burger King
Comcast
Ron Brown
Toyota
Tylenol
Urban League Gates
Wal-Mart

SECTION THREE

Closing The Deal

OVERVIEW

Get your pen out because this will be your most intensive month yet. This month is all about creating the perfect essay. It's no secret that the essay can basically make or break your application. Knowing how to articulate your achievements in a manner that is both grammatically correct and creative can be difficult. This month's activities are designed to help you shape the perfect essay.

I already know what you are thinking. You hate writing essays, right? Relax. There is indeed a science to writing essays that count. Unlike the essays that you submit for your English class, scholarship essays can actually be fun to write, because you are encouraged to include as much of your personality as possible.

Your number one priority is to make the scholarship committee remember your application out of the pile of 100, 1000, or even 10,000 other applicants. The essay is your primary opportunity to prove to the committee why you are a worthy investment. Why should they give you $10,000?

In this section you will find a few examples of winning essays. Good luck!

LESSON ONE

Breaking Down The Scholarship Essay

This week, using your determined scholarship profile, begin to organize the main points of your essay. Creating an outline will help to guide your thoughts, so that they will flow properly throughout the essay. There is nothing worse than an essay that is filled with jumbled thoughts that are hard to follow. When creating your outline, jot down your first three ideas. These are the typical responses, the ones that at least 100 applicants will focus on. Now dig deeper. Think about a more creative approach that would grab the reader's attention.

It is often helpful if you begin your scholarship essay with the end in mind. What is it that you really want the scholarship committee to know about you? What message are you attempting to convey? How can you prove to them that you are a perfect fit for their criteria?

Create an outline for your essay.

Activity 6:
Create an outline for your essay

The first part of outlining your scholarship essay is making sure you provide a solid answer to the question! You have to prove to the scholarship committee that you are a perfect fit for their criteria. One easy way to do this is to create an eligibility checklist like the one below.

Eligibility Requirements	My Good Fit Factors
1. Applicant Must Demonstrate Strong Leadership Abilities	As president of The FBLA, I have devoted a large portion of my time to challenging my peers to cultivate their own leadership skills.
2. Applicant Must Be Able To Articulate Their Career Goals	Ten years from now, I plan to run one of the largest minority-owned engineering firms in the country.
3. Applicant Must Possess A Solid Commitment to Civic Engagement	Because less than 15% of the engineering field is comprised of African-American males, I will use my background in development to launch a program that will encourage black males to use their innate analytical skills in a more productive manner.

Activity 6 *(Continued)*:
Your "good fit" qualities

Based on the eligibility criteria, provide 2 to 3 specific examples of your winning characteristics.

Eligibility Requirements	My Good Fit Factors
1.	
2.	
3.	

Activity 7:
Your key messages

Like many students, you might have a hard time starting your essay. Instead of jumping right in, it might be better to ease into it by identifying the key points you'd like to convey.

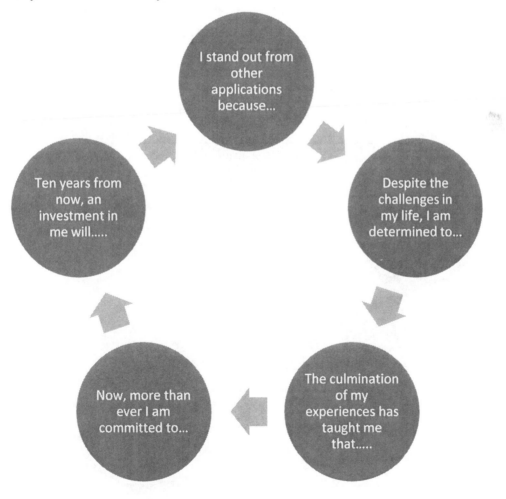

Your Scholarship Profile

List the Three Top Messages You Want To Convey To The Scholarship Committee

1. _____

_____

2. _____

_____

3. _____

_____

Activity 8:
Your "investment factor"

Who will you be in the next 10 years that is worth their investment?

_____

_____

_____

_____

_____

_____

_____

_____

_____

_____

_____

_____

_____

_____

_____

LESSON TWO

Nailing the Scholarship Community Service Essay

O ne of the most popular essay prompts for scholarship competitions is the community service essay. Organizations want to know what you have done that is worth their financial investment. Now, more than ever, companies and foundations are looking for the growth potential of their dollars. In short, they want to know that the money they give you towards your education has the long-term ability to impact the lives of hundreds after you graduate.

On the next page will find a sample essay written by one of our top scholarship winners that highlights a few elements that will make your community service essay stand out.

Sample Community Service Essay

Police Brutality. Ever since the Rodney King beatings and the Amadou Diallo trial, this phrase has been on the tips of the tongues of politicians and civil rights activists across the country. Suburban Americans were appalled as they watched the violence unfold on their television screens, but for children who grew up in urban communities, the realities of police brutality are a little too close to home.

Including current events to your essay adds more relevance for the reader.

I live in a community in southeast Washington, DC known as Barry Farms, a neighborhood notorious for its high crime and drug infestation. Police brutality had become as common as the graffiti that surrounded our neighborhood walls. As a teenager, I felt somewhat helpless as I watched police exert unnecessary force on youth who had no voice. Luckily, I remembered the training that I had received through the Justice for DC Youth Coalition, and I decided to transform my feelings of vulnerability into action. I quickly discovered that other youth shared my opinions, and we began to brainstorm ideas. What evolved was a massive "Know Your Rights" campaign.

Even if you worked on your project with a group, it's important to highlight your leadership/ responsibilities within the project.

We compiled our interviews, personal stories, and legal research into a magazine called, "Is It Because..." I was primarily responsible *for conducting interviews with the police, researching amendments to citizens' rights, and developing a youth training workshop. I also helped to develop* a public service announcement and I devoted my weekends to distributing the magazine to local youth organizations, the police department, schools and the Mayor's office.

Scholarship committees need to be able to "connect the dots." Don't forget to include what inspired you.

My initial passion for the "Know Your Rights" campaign was rooted in the urgency that I felt to protect my brother, age 17, and his friends. Too often I had witnessed humility's swift transition to anger create dangerous situations. I wanted to do more than just place a band-aid on this sore spot in my neighborhood. I was determined to begin the process of healing.

There are still opportunities to highlight your "winning characteristics" within the community service essay. Don't be afraid to brag on yourself!

My diligence finally paid off when I was asked to testify during a judicial hearing before the city council about the impact of police brutality on youth. *This project did more than help me gain a sense of empowerment from knowing that I was capable of using my knowledge to affect change. It re-established my sense of hope for my community. This feeling will stay with me as I transition into adulthood. I now realize that education is more than just the passport to the future. It is the foundation for the advancement of justice, a concept that can not be taken for granted.*

Your "lessons learned" moments provide the committee with a keen insight on your potential.

Before this project, I did not believe in the power of my voice. I take great pride in knowing that my efforts will one day save the life of a young person who knows their rights. To me, there is no greater reward for service.

Activity 8:
Draft a 500-word community service essay

_____

_____

_____

_____

_____

_____

_____

_____

_____

_____

_____

_____

_____

_____

_____

_____

_____

LESSON THREE

Mastering The Career Goals Essay

T he career goals essay is also another major topic that allows scholarship committees to get a glimpse of your "it" factor. Beyond your professional aspirations, this essay is truly a demonstration of your level of preparation, your awareness of the world around you, and your overall ability to succeed in a college atmosphere.

Read the career goals essay below, and highlight the statements that stand out the most. This student, who received a UNCF scholarship, was able to use his career goals essay to demonstrate the following:

1. An understanding of the world around him

Fear... Panic... Insecurity. Each of these terms have been on the tips of our tongues and etched in the backs of our minds for the last year. For many, these words may have invaded our workplaces, our families, our lives. As the entire world watches the uncertainty of the economic climate, for young people in particular there is one thing that is certain; America's notion of job security has definitely been shaken to its core.

As a young black male who is on the threshold of his academic pursuits, my mind has been inundated with images of mass company layoffs and the plight of families who "took the safe route" by securing jobs in corporate America. Our nation's old formula for success is in many ways no longer valid, and as I prepare to enter college I realize that I must carve out my own pathways to financial stability. I refuse to conform to the rhetoric of "corporate safety." Instead, I choose to take these economic times as a sign that now, more than ever, my passions have the power to direct my plans. Armed with a new sense of determination, I am eagerly exploring entrepreneurship as my gateway to success.

2. His inspiration for pursuing a particular field

My introduction to the world of entrepreneurship actually stems from a source close to home. For years I have watched as my mother, the founder of a nonprofit organization that prepares students in underserved communities for college, toil over marketing plans, budgets and event logistics. It was indeed in her smallest victories that I discovered the true essence of entrepreneurship.

3. His ability to take initiative and serve as a leader amongst his peers

As the key youth liaison for her program, I have assisted in the planning and preparation of their national college tours and organized youth focus groups to ensure the youth perspective was effectively maintained. It was my idea to institute a dress code for the Los Angeles venue so that my peers would take the opportunity to speak to college representatives more seriously. With each year that I participate in the planning of these events, I become more aware of the opportunities for me to pursue my academic and professional goals. My experiences with my mom's nonprofit organization have not only strengthened my desire to excel in college. They have also served as the foundation of my desire to use my talents and resources to impact the lives of others. As I prepare to embark upon perhaps the most important phase in my life, I recognize that it is the culmination of my experiences, my passions, and my dreams that will ultimately set the tone for my future.

4. His proven commitment to his chosen field

Last summer I was selected out of 175 students to participate in a 6-week business academy, the University of LaVerne Summer Business Camp. Through this program, I learned how to create a business plan and develop realistic budgets and marketing strategies. I also learned that for many entrepreneurs, success was merely a by-product of preparation and ingenuity. This knowledge led to the establishment of my first production company called ABC Productions Along with two business partners, I have hosted a series of social dance productions throughout the Inland Empire for teens ages 13-17. Our initial goal for the dance productions was to create a positive social atmosphere for teens. Our first dance production was "standing room" only with close to 300 teens in attendance. With the business experience I gathered from my summer camp and working different jobs, I was thoroughly equipped to handle my responsibilities of developing both a marketing plan and a tactical plan to execute the events.

Some of the challenges I knew we would face immediately were the marketing challenges, especially since we were starting without a budget. Using my knowledge of identifying niche markets, I designed a plan to select popular students at area high schools to help us spread the word, and I launched a comprehensive internet campaign. It is no secret that nationally, the high school dropout rate is 77%. Activities such as these dances provide youth with an opportunity communicate in a positive environment among other teens who have goals of going to college and being socially responsible. By allowing youth to feel connected to a common goal, I believe that I am, in some small way, brightening the futures of my peers.

5. His level of determination

Overall, my experiences with the production company have served as a testament to the power of youthful vision and persistence, proof that anything I commit myself to is possible. As I prepare to one day own a sports management firm, I am confident that business ventures such as my production company will serve as key stepping stones for my career as a sports agent.

6. His ability to leave a lasting impact on his chosen field

True to my entrepreneurial spirit, my vision is to establish a company that will promote excellence within the sports management field, ensuring that my clients share in my commitment to enhancing the lives of others. My sports management firm will be different from most because we will take a special interest in our athletes beyond the playing field. We will offer tips on money management and design a plan for them to have money long after their professional career has ended. In addition, I plan to offer internships and summer programs for aspiring young people who want to pursue a career in the sports industry. I will also donate regularly to charitable organizations that help underserved youth achieve their dreams. To me, true success is more than simply "making it" in life. My ultimate goal is to plant entrepreneurial seeds that operate with integrity in the hearts and minds of the next generation so that we can reconstruct the American image of success. Twenty years from now, I want my children to believe in their power to create independent wealth opportunities, to own corporations and manage their own financial portfolios. This is, after all, the true benefit of entrepreneurship; to dream, to hope, to believe.

Which Statements Stood Out To You? What were the key *Investment Factors?*

1. _____

2. _____

3. _____

Activity 10:
Create a 500-word
career goals essay

LESSON FOUR

Sealing The Deal

As you can see, there is a clear difference between writing that will score a high grade in your English class, and writing that will score a $10,000 scholarship. In most instances, the committee will decide whether or not to strongly consider your application within the first few sentences of your essay. Check out the following Creative Openers, and guess which one actually won the scholarship.

Sample Creative Openers
Which One Is A Winner?

1. As a third generation artist, I grew up admiring the sculptures and oil pastels that lined the walls of my home. I would watch my mother take a blank canvas and tempera paints along with her other favorite mediums, and create what I thought were the most beautiful paintings in the world.

2. Volunteering is a wonderful way to make a difference in your community or in someone's life. I've volunteered many times over the years, but there's one volunteer project that I can never forget. I volunteered with an organization called Christmas in April.

3. "Dance is the loftiest, the most moving, the most beautiful of the arts because it no more translation or abstract from life it is life itself." —Havelock Ellis

4. I have a diversity of interests. None of them affected me as much as dance. My parents are of West Indian descent, so they made sure I had a deep appreciation of our culture, traditions and ambition.

5. I have lived in the same neighborhood for fourteen years. In my neighborhood, most of the dreams of youth included becoming entertainers, actors, rappers, singers, basketball or football players. I, on the other hand, have dreamed to become a veterinarian. For as long as I could remember, I have wanted to work with and around animals. Around the age of seven I began to explore my interest in animals and veterinary medicine, reading everything I could get hands on. Every month I would collect a series of cards from "Wildlife Adventure Card" which had fun and interesting facts.

6. Bang! Bang! The gun went off and we all ducked. It was the boys from Southeast coming to start trouble with us again. Two years ago my brother got shot and ever since them we have been at war with them.

The first prompt is a winner, because it accomplishes one simple task; It makes the reader want to know more. Your first paragraph could be only opportunity you will have to make the reader "connect" to your application. Make it count!

Activity 11:
Add a creative opening to your career goals and community service essays

Section Three Wrap-Up

Whew! All of the worksheets and activities in this scholarship workbook were designed to prepare you to be the most competitive scholarship applicant possible. Our goal was truly to help you develop a comprehensive college funding strategy by simply giving you the blueprint for *putting a process to the process.* You've built your scholarship profile, designed your scholarship brag project, navigated the scholarship research maze, and crafted a winning essay. Now there's only one thing left for you to do... Win! Win! Win!

Be sure to check out our website at www.scholarshipacademy.org and join us on Facebook (Scholarship Academy) and Twitter (@scholarshipacad) for updated tips and resources.

JESSICA'S EXTRAS

ESSAY TIPS

Tip # 1
Learn how to sell yourself. Try to avoid simply putting your resume in paragraph form.

The essay is the only opportunity that you have to *sell yourself*. Most students will simply list activities they were involved in, such as student council or band, without much consideration for the bragging points associated with these activities. As student council president, what changes did you implement that will have a lasting impact on your peers? What leadership qualities did you learn from band that will prepare you as you transition to college? Thinking beyond your titles, the number of years, or even the number of hours you've been a part of a particular organization will help you tap into a creative answer that will stand out from your competitors.

Tip # 2
Use imagery to create a mental picture of your accomplishments.

The biggest mistake that most students make is trying to cram all of their activities into one essay. Focus on one or two key activities (based on your activity matrix) that you can describe in detail. There is a big difference between *showing* and telling. Instead of telling the committee that you are a leader, show them the number of families impacted by your annual food drive, or the amount of money you raised for sickle cell research. Remember, this is a competition. Using imagery is a great way to capture the reader's attention, especially in the beginning of your essay. If they get a mental picture of your vision for your life, they're likely to be hooked!

Tip # 3

Be careful of the image you are portraying to the scholarship committee.

Even if you got off to a slow start in high school, avoid statements such as, " I didn't really apply myself," or my personal favorite, "If my mother hadn't made me..." The worst thing you can do is cause the scholarship committee to lose confidence in your ability to succeed. Try not to mention your weakness or shortcomings, unless you are specifically asked to do so. Keep in mind that while you are exposing your faults, another applicant is probably bragging about their accomplishments.

Tip # 4

Share a "Lesson Learned" moment with the committee

You've worked hard to complete your scholarship brag project. Let your passion show by adding examples of your personal growth to further prove the impact that your project had. After the scholarship committee has read about 100 other applicants' canned food drives, tutoring programs and neighborhood clean-up projects, your ability to share a deeper awareness of your project results will help push you beyond *just the facts* and into the realm of quality competition.

Remember, no matter how skilled you are in writing, it is always a good idea to allow someone to review your work to catch mistakes. Keep in mind that for scholarship essays, grammar is everything and perfection is a must!

TIPS FOR PARENTS

Tip # 1

Make sure your child applies for the appropriate awards.

The quickest way for your child to be eliminated from a scholarship competition is not meeting one of the requirements. Help your child research scholarships that fit her profile.

Tip # 2

Getting involved is key.

Organizations such as the Beta Club, the NAACP, the National Urban League, and the National Honor Society provide scholarships for their members. Linking up with these organizations early will help your child build his resume and increase his scholarship pool.

Tip # 3

Have your child maximize his eligibility.

We all have passions. Using those passions to help others will make your child more attractive to scholarship committees. Most scholarship committees are looking for students who have found creative ways to give back to their community. For project ideas to help your child maximize his eligibility, visit www.thevolunteercenter.org or www.youthbuild.org.

Tip # 4

Teach your child how to minimize her playing field.

To find those awards that will best fit your child's profile, start small and build on it. Consider categories such as her major or specialization, city and state of residence, special conditions or disabilities, and her organization involvement. The scholarships in these smaller more specific categories are generally less competitive, which increases your child's chance of winning.

Tip # 5

Show your child how to write right.

The essay can basically make or break your application. Use it as an opportunity for your child to brag on himself (but make sure he tells the truth) and prove to the scholarship committee what sets him apart from the other applicants. Tailor the essay so it directly addresses their criteria, and most importantly ANSWER THE QUESTION! The most important thing to remember is that it is never too late to find scholarships. It just takes a little research on your part.

For more information, or to work directly with Jessica Johnson to develop a scholarship portfolio, visit www.scholarshipacademy.org.

FAVORITE SCHOLARSHIPS

- **Coca-Cola Scholars Foundation, Inc.** The applicant must be a high school senior attending a school in a participating Coca-Cola bottler's territory. Contact Coca-Cola to find out where bottlers' territories are located. Candidates are evaluated on character, individual merit, and background.
  INFO http:// www.coca-colascholars.org.
  ADDRESS Coca-Cola Scholars Foundation, P.O. Box 442, Atlanta, GA 30301
  PHONE 800-306-2653

- **Do Something Brick Awards** The Do Something Brick Awards provides a $5,000 scholarship and a $5,000 grant to *change-makers,* age 18 and under, who work with Do Something to improve their communities. A $10,000 grant is available to those aged 19-25.
  INFO brick@dosomething.org

- **KFC Colonel's Scholars** This program is looking for high school seniors with financial need and an entrepreneurial spirit. Awards are up to $20,000 for tuition, fees, textbooks, room and board. To qualify, graduating high school seniors must: earn a minimum high school cumulative GPA of 2.75; enroll in a public college or university within your state of legal residence; plan to pursue a bachelor's degree; be a U.S. citizen or permanent resident; and demonstrate financial need.
  INFO www.kfcscholars.org

- **Gates Millennium Scholars Program** This scholarship is open to seniors who are African American, American Indian/Alaska Native, Asian Pacific Islander American or Hispanic American. Applicants must be citizens or legal permanent residents of the United States and have at least a 3.3 GPA; have demonstrated leadership through school or community service; and meet Federal Pell Grant eligibility criteria (low income).
  INFO/APPLY http://www.gmsp.org

- **Tom Joyner Foundation Full Ride Scholarship** The Full Ride Scholarship will be given away to a high school senior with a minimum grade point average of 3.50 and a minimum SAT score of 1300 (math and verbal only) or ACT score of 28. The applicant must have been accepted into an HBCU. The scholarship will recognize academic distinction, as well as strong character and personal qualities.
  INFO www.blackamericaweb.com

- **The Horatio Alger Scholarship** The Horatio Alger Association seeks to assist students who have demonstrated perseverance in overcoming adversity; strength of character; financial need; a good academic record; commitment to pursue a college education; and a desire to contribute to society.
  INFO/APPLY www.horatioalger.org/scholarships

- **The Girls Going Places Scholarship** Sponsored by Guardian Life Insurance Company of America, this program awards prizes totaling $30,000 to 15 girls, age 12 to 18, who have demonstrated budding entrepreneurship. There is one first place award of $10,000, one second place award of $5,000, one third place award of $3,000 and twelve $1,000 awards.
  INFO www.glic.com

- **QuestBridge National College Match Program** This program helps outstanding low-income high school seniors gain admission and full four-year scholarships to some of the nation's most selective colleges.
  INFO/APPLY www.questbridge.org

- **Ron Brown Scholar Program** This scholarship is awarded to academically talented, highly motivated African American students who are seniors in high school this year and plan to pursue undergraduate degrees full time. Students must be U.S. citizens or hold permanent resident visa cards.
  INFO www.ronbrown.org

- **NFIB Young Entrepreneur Award** The National Federation of Independent Business offers this $1,000 scholarship to recognize students who have demonstrated entrepreneurial spirit and initiative, such as starting his or her own business, and who have participation in organizations such as DECA, Future Business Leaders of America and Junior Achievement, among others, or through other initiatives. Applicants must locate a dues paying member of the NFIB for nomination following the completion of application materials and an essay.
  INFO www.nfib.com

- **Kohl's Kids Who Care Program** The Kohl's Kids Who Care Program is an annual opportunity to recognize and reward students, age 6 to 18, who volunteer in their communities. Awards range from Kohl's $50 gift cards to $5,000 scholarships toward college. Nomination forms are available beginning February 1 at any Kohl's Department Store or from the Kohl's website (see below) and can be returned to any Kohl's customer service desk.
  INFO/APPLY www.kohlscorporation.com

- **MetroPCS Community Scholars Program** MetroPCS and Kyocera Communications, Inc., a leading global manufacturer of wireless phones and devices, are awarding $2,500 scholarships to high school seniors who plan to continue education in college or university programs. The overarching criteria will be students who have demonstrated exceptional involvement in volunteerism and community service, in addition to academics and other criteria.
  INFO/APPLY www.metropcs.com/scholarship

- **Bonner Scholars Program** The Bonner Foundation provides four-year community service scholarships of up to $4,000 a year to 1,500 students each year at 25 colleges and universities. The Bonner Scholars, in turn, commit 10 hours per week to volunteer service and participate in a summer community service internship.
  INFO www.bonner.org

- **Comcast Leaders and Achievers Scholarship Program** The Comcast Leaders and Achievers Scholarship Program, formerly the Comcast Foundation Leaders of Tomorrow Scholarship Program, awards more than one thousand $1,000 scholarships for community service and leadership to high school seniors in communities served by Comcast. Candidates must be nominated by their high school principals by mid-March. Each principal may nominate only one student.
  INFO http://www.comcast.com/corporate/about/inthecommunity/partners/leadersandachievers.html

- **Gloria Barron Prize for Young Heroes** The Gloria Barron Prize for Young Heroes is awarded annually to ten U.S. and Canadian students, aged 8- 18, who have developed an extraordinary service project that helped people and the planet. Half of the winners are focused on helping their communities and people, and half are focused on protecting the environment. Winners receive a $2,000 scholarship.
  INFO www.barronprize.org

- **Discover Card Tribute Award** Applicants must be high school juniors and pursuing post-secondary education or training at an accredited institution, with a minimum GPA of 2.75. Applicants must demonstrate accomplishments in community service, display leadership, and have faced a significant roadblock or challenge.
  INFO http://www.discoverfinancial.com/community/scholarship.shtml

- **Emma Bowen Foundation** The Emma L. Bowen Foundation scholarship was created to prepare minority youth for careers in the media industry. Minority students with a cumulative grade point average of 3.0 or better and an interest in the media industry as a career are eligible to apply. Students earn an hourly salary and matching funds for college expenses.
  INFO www.emmabowenfoundation.com

- **Nordstrom Scholarship** Nordstrom is committed to the communities where we do business. Helping students achieve their dreams of higher education is a meaningful way for us to show that commitment. Since 1994, we have selected hard-working high school students to receive $10,000 college scholarships. Today, with educational funding becoming an even greater challenge than ever, we have expanded our scholarship program and are pleased to help 80 outstanding students across the country take the next step toward achieving their goals
INFO http://shop.nordstrom.com/c/nordstrom-cares-scholarship

- **Best Buy** The Best Buy Scholarship program rewards students for their volunteer efforts and work experience in addition to academic achievements. The grants aim to help exceptional students to further their education and experience with a college education. 1500 Students are selected to receive awards of $1,500 each; 50 students will receive awards of $10,000 each.
INFO http://www.bestbuy-communityrelations.com/scholarship.htm

- **AXA Achievement Scholarship Program** The AXA Achievement Scholarship Program awards $10,000 and $25,000 scholarships to high school seniors who have demonstrated outstanding achievement in non-academic activities in school, the community or the workplace. The award is sponsored by the AXA Foundation. US citizenship or legal residency is required. There are 52 winners of $10,000 scholarships. Ten national winners will receive an additional $15,000, for a total of $25,000.
INFO www.axa-achievement.com

- **Burger King Scholars Program** This $1000 scholarship is open to seniors with a 2.5 or higher GPA – who work part-time – are actively involved in community service and demonstrate financial need.
INFO/APPLY www.bk.com/scholars

NOTES

JESSICA D. JOHNSON

Hard work and creativity are two words that have characterized much of Jessica Johnson's life. The 2004 summa cum laude Howard graduate says that her inspiration comes from James 2:26, "Faith without works is dead!" Since the age of 13, Jessica has been developing programs that have had an impact on her community. She began by writing and producing morality plays for the local theatre and creating an African dance troupe to promote cultural awareness amongst her peers. At age 15, Jessica launched her first radio talk show, entitled *Teen Talk,* to provide the youth in her community with an opportunity to express their opinions. She also started a column in her local newspaper entitled *Teens Speak*. Jessica's efforts received national attention when she was selected as a "Point-of-View Journalist" for Oxygen Media's Digital Trackers show in 1999. For two years she hosted and produced mini-documentaries for the nationally-syndicated television network.

Jessica's undying love for her community followed her to Howard University. While at Howard, she served as the 2002-2003 Miss School of Communications, and was a member of the Annenberg Honors Program As a recipient of more than **$200,000 in scholarships**.

Jessica created her own business, The Minority Scholarship Quest Program, in which she serves as a family scholarship consultant and travels throughout the country conducting scholarship workshops for organizations such as The Southern Christian Leadership Conference (SCLC), The U.S. Department of Labor, The New York Urban League, and the National Center of Philanthropy.

Jessica has served as a member of numerous scholarship selection committees, including the Howard University Alumni Scholarship committee, and she has developed a comprehensive scholarship workbook. To date, The Minority Scholarship Quest Program boasts a 100% college acceptance rate. From 2009–2011, the program helped students secure more than $4.5 million in scholarships, earning them recognition on the *Oprah Winfrey Show* and features in publications such as *U.S. News and World Report, Ebony* magazine and *The Washington Post* for their outstanding community service initiatives. Because of her involvement, Jessica has received numerous awards including the Discover Card Tribute Award, the JC Penney Golden Rule Award, and the Women Leaders in Government Relations Foundation Award. She has been featured in *Black Enterprise,* the *Black Issues in Higher Education Magazine,* the *NAACP Crisis Magazine* and on the cover of *react* magazine. She is also a feature writer for HBCUconnect.com.

So what's in store for this dynamic trailblazer? With a master's degree in Public Administration, she has established a nonprofit segment of her business called The Scholarship Academy, which assists low-income and first-generation students in developing unique scholarship profiles through weekly curriculum-based sessions. Johnson hopes one day to create a scholarship fund for minority students.

For more information about The Minority Scholarship Quest Program and The Scholarship Academy, visit www.minorityscholarshipquest.org and www. scholarshipacademy.org.

Key Speaking Topics: *Discovering The Keys To Scholarship Success, Selecting A College That's Right For You, Leadership That Counts, The Value of a HBCU Education, Entrepreneurship, Identifying Your Passions, and many more!*

THE
SCHOLARSHIP
ACADEMY

About The Scholarship Academy

Civic Engagement
Leadership Exploration
Social Entrepreneurship Training

The Scholarship Academy (TSA) was created in January 2006 by Howard University graduate Jessica Johnson, a recipient of more than $200,000 in scholarships. TSA specializes in breaking down the scholarship acquisition process into realistic terms for low-income and first-generation students. Early preparation and intense personal development are at the heart of The Scholarship Academy's program initiatives. Through a series of curriculum-based activities, our program partners with schools, churches, and nonprofit organizations to help them develop strategies for scholarship success.

TSA has developed a unique structure for the scholarship process that is more comparable to the SAT test-taking approach, where strategies and personal development outweigh random scholarship selections. Our underlying strength is our ability to engage *average* students in using principles like youth entrepreneurship, exceptional community service endeavors, and leadership exploration to make vital connections between passions, service to others, and funding opportunities. We teach families to look beyond GPA, financial status and social backgrounds so that they can effectively explore eligibility enhancers to fill financial gaps.

The proof is in the numbers. By equipping students with the necessary tools to recognize their *scholarship selling points* and engaging students in developing *activities that matter*, TSA's staff assisted our students in securing more than $4.5 million in scholarships!

Our List of Student Awards Includes:

- ✓ 8 DC Achievers Scholars ($50,000)
- ✓ 3 Gates Millennium Scholars (Full Ride)
- ✓ 3 AXA Achievement Scholars ($10,000)
- ✓ 2 Children's Defense Fund Awards ($10,000)
- ✓ 4 Prudential Spirit Awards ($10,000)
- ✓ 2 Posse Scholars (Full Ride)

- ✓ 1 Frederick Douglass Scholar (Full Ride)
- ✓ 6 KFC Scholars ($20,000)
- ✓ 1 Servant Leader Award ($10,000)
- ✓ 1 Yoshiyama Youth Service Award ($5000)
- ✓ 1 Atlanta Braves Award ($1000)
- ✓ 1 Burger King Scholar ($1000)

Our Scholarship Mini Boot Camp Series

Using The Scholarship Workbook, The Scholarship Academy helps hundreds of students design realistic college funding options each year.

Boot Camp Topics (4 Core Sessions)

Session I – Identifying Your Scholarship Profile

- **Setting The Stage** *Icebreakers, Introductions, Overview of Activities, What does it take to win? – Student Scenarios, Skills Assessments, Profile Development*

Session II – Maximizing Your Eligibility

- **Maximizing Your Eligibility** *Exploring Characteristics of A Winner*
- **Scholarship BRAG Project Design**

Session III – Navigating The Scholarship Research Maze

- **Navigating The Financial Aid Maze** – *Intro to The Scholarship Search Method*
- **Scholarship Scavenger Hunt**- *Tailor-made list of resources*

Session IV – Crafting A Winning Essay

- **Warm-Up** – *Journal Entry, My Career Footprints, Creation of Scholarship Calendars, Lingo Game*
- **Tackling The Scholarship Essay** - *Creative Openers, Sentence Prompts, Sample Winning Essays*
- **Mock Scholarship Committee Activity**
- **The Science of Essay Writing**
- **Sealing The Deal** – *Application DOs and DON'Ts*

Class Take-Aways

Each participant in The Scholarship Boot Camp Course receives the following:

1. **Scholarship Brag Project design** (Identification of Scholarship Profile)
2. Tailored List of **15-20 "good fit" scholarship options**
3. **Three core essay reviews** (leadership and/or significant experience, career goals, community involvement)
4. **Strategies to create tailored, competitive application packages**

To register for an upcoming Scholarship Boot Camp, visit our website at www.scholarshipacademy.org or call 470-355-1732 today!

Atlanta, GA Office
50 Hurt Plaza, Suite 860
Atlanta, GA 30303
Phone 470-355-1732

www.scholarshipacademy.org
inquiries@scholarshipacademy.org